MY SISTER AND I

The Diary of
a Dutch Boy Refugee

by

Dirk van der Heide

TRANSLATED BY
MRS. ANTOON DEVENTER

NEW YORK
HARCOURT, BRACE AND COMPANY

D
811.5
H4

21155

10/17/41 Apple Tree #0.75

INTRODUCTION

DIRK VAN DER HEIDE is a Dutch boy, from the outskirts of Rotterdam, who lived through the five-day blitzkrieg in Holland. He is twelve years old; a sturdy boy with straight taffy-colored hair that falls over his forehead, mild blue eyes, and a smile that quickly lights up his rather solemn face. His real name is not Dirk van der Heide and the names in the diary have all been changed in order to protect his family.

Dirk has added to the diary since he left Holland. The English captain on the boat that brought Dirk to America could read Dutch, and persuaded him to write his experiences in more detail. Dirk was able to reconstruct some of the record on shipboard. He did so without self-consciousness; it is certain that Dirk himself has no realization of how remarkable and how significant the diary really is.

The effect of Dirk's observations is to give a sense of what war means to an impressionable child's mind. His days in the Rotterdam bomb-

3

ings, his escape to England, and his voyage to America are the experiences in these troubled times of thousands of people, young and old. The headlong plunge of a peaceful people into disaster, and all the aftermath of courage, terror, suffering, and sacrifice that this Dutch boy describes belong to the history of the present. They belong also to the future of the children who have experienced such early shocks of blitzkrieg.

It is clear to anyone who reads this diary that Dirk is a remarkable boy. Sometimes his writing seems abnormally mature, and sometimes plainly the statement of a healthy and naive child. He has no awareness of unusual ability, and doesn't seem to have any instinct for showing off. For us, the message of the diary is in its simple statements, and the humor, courage, and pathos which we can read into it. Here the bewildered child in wartime is revealed with a direct force and clarity that will make grown-ups use the term "modern civilization" with painful misgivings, even though this revelation also restores faith in the strength of innocence under the worst kind of fire.

MRS. ANTOON DEVENTER

I AM keeping my diary again because of my mother and because of the English Captain. I'm sorry I haven't written anything for so long. There have been many things to do and everything is so strange I haven't even thought much about my diary.

The English Captain has read the part of my diary about the war and he says it is very good but short and I should go back over it and write down all I remember and about my family. I am going to try but I don't like to think about the war but the Captain says people ought to know what it's really like so that they won't let it happen any more. I sit at the Captain's table every day and he is very kind and laughing. We talk about Holland and when he was there and about the war. Everyone talks about the war, although everyone tries not to.

My mother helped me start my diary when I was nine years old. She wanted me to keep it faithfully, always. Mother's name was Marta. She was killed by a bomb the second day of the cruel war. My father is a doctor to animals and is still in Holland.

I do not remember everything that happened when the Nazis came so it will be hard for me to go back over my diary. Some things I remember very well, especially the bombs. There were many fires and much smoke and noise. Sometimes I hardly remember anything else. Keetje remembers things too. She is my sister and is nine years old while I am twelve and two months. We are going to America because of the war and this is our eighth day on the ocean.

There are many children on this boat going to America. There is an English boy named Jack who is my age. He has very good manners. Most of the children are English and they cannot understand Keetje and me so very well. We studied English in school but it sounds different when the English talk. Keetje never

mentions Mother and neither do I but I know
how she feels. She sits and stares often and is
quiet. She never was quiet before the war.
Keetje is very pretty like Mother. Mother was
a Frisian from North Holland. They are all tall
and handsome and speak a different language.
Keetje used to be very fat and I was afraid
she would be just a fatty. She has lost many
pounds this last month and looks all right
again but too pale, the Captain says. Some of
the English children look pale too. Keetje is
homesick I think but she is very brave and
doesn't cry before anybody. I wish our Mother
could have come with us. Some of the English children have mothers or nurses or gran-
nies, but not all.

The Captain has promised to read my diary
when it is finished. He knows a great many
Dutch words but not for talking, not as many
as I know of English, nor as many as Keetje.
Keetje calls the Captain Uncle because his
name is Peter and our Uncle's name is Pieter,
spelled that way. I told Keetje to call him Mr.
or Mijnheer Captain but she goes on calling

7

him Uncle and the Captain doesn't seem to mind.

The Uncle we are going to in America is named Klaas. Before the war he imported things from Holland to America. I hope he will be glad to see us. Uncle Pieter said he would be. Keetje and I didn't want to come to America but our Father was fighting and Uncle Pieter told us it was best. I wanted to take care of Father's animals. We cried because we didn't get to say good-by to Father. Uncle Pieter cried too when we left him in England. He is the only man I ever saw cry. Keetje says she doesn't believe Uncle Pieter really cried because he was waving and smiling but then she never believes me except when I swear it. He did cry, but not out loud. He looked very pale and I think he was cross and tired after the trip from Rotterdam to Zeeland and all that happened to us before we got to England. We were tired too but Uncle Pieter is quite old, about fifty. He swears a great deal. He calls the Germans "fat swine." Uncle Pieter is quite fat himself but he hates the Germans for what they are doing to our country and to all the other little countries. Uncle Pieter was in the last war because his wife who is dead is a Belgian. He lost four fingers on his left hand when he was fighting and that is another reason why he hates the Germans. His right hand is fine.

My name is Dirk van der Heide. This I'm sticking in for you, Captain, because I don't believe you know my last name or much about my home. My home is just on the edge of Rotterdam. We live so far out because my Father is a veterinary and that means he works with animals who live farther out. I heard my Father say once he liked to doctor animals better than people. My Mother asked him why but I never heard his answer. He just shrugged, I think. He is not a great talker. I have gone with him many times to help with a sick cow or horse and sometimes dogs. Keetje has never gone even once but she would have some day if we had stayed at home.

The German Nazis came on May 10th and surprised everyone except my Father and

Uncle Pieter. Uncle Pieter said he had known it all along, "the damned swine." He said it many times and was angry. It is too bad my Uncle Pieter is not the General instead of General Winkelman although he is a good General but quite old. My mother would never have been killed if Uncle Pieter had been General.

Maybe Uncle Pieter and my Father were not the only people who knew about the war coming. There were many soldiers going around. They must have known or they wouldn't have been soldiers. I told Uncle Pieter this but he said, "Soldiers, what do they know." They wore greenish-brown uniforms, very handsome. Keetje was in *love* with a soldier on our street who took her for a piggy-back ride once. He was a marine and could fight on land or sea. I don't know how many soldiers we had before the war but Uncle Pieter said there were 450,000 ready and more than a million who would go when the time came. That's a lot. He always said the Nazis and Hitler had a great many more, "the damned cowardly swine." We were in Belgium when we heard that our country had been forced to surrender to the Nazis. When people talked about traitors Uncle Pieter got very angry. "Traitors, traitors. That didn't do it. The Nazis had more men, more tanks, more planes. Maybe there were a few traitors but the Nazis won because they were stronger and that's all there is to it 'the damned swine.'" My mother never liked the way my Uncle swore before Keetje and me but my Father always laughed. He is very fond of Uncle Pieter. Keetje and I talked about them both until very late last night. It must have been ten o'clock or maybe more. Keetje sleeps in a lower bunk so she won't fall out when the waves are high and the boat rocks.

THIS is what I wrote in my diary before, changed some and longer because of the English Captain.

Keetje did not go to school today. Mother told me to tell Mijnheer Zoon, her teacher, that she had a bad cold. It has been raining for several days. When I read about other countries it seems to me it rains more in Holland than anywhere else but I don't know. The summer we spent in Brittany seemed just as bad.

Father went over to the Baron's early this morning to visit the stables. The Baron's favorite riding horse has worms or something. Father and the Baron are friends but Father dislikes the Baron sometimes for he never pays his bills promptly and there is no reason why for his house is a big brick house bigger than ours and he is rich. We are not rich but well to do. We have two kindermaids and a cook for Mother and for Keetje and me though I don't need a nurse any longer and haven't for *years*. One kindermaid is named Betje and one Brenda. Brenda is very gentle and good. Our cook, Mother says, is neither gentle nor good but she is a fine cook. She makes wonderful poffertjes, which are little fried cakes. She smokes cigars too.

There were many soldiers on the Boompjes when I went through on my way to school. They were all around all the public buildings. I asked Father why and he said he didn't know but maybe the papers would say. The papers didn't say, for Father went right away and looked in the *Telegraaf*. He read aloud to me that Prince Bernhard zu Lippe-Biesterfeld— he's the Crown Princess Juliana's husband— visited the military headquarters at The Hague and that the war in Norway was bad for the Allies except in Narvik. I looked up Narvik on my map and found it is a town very far north. Norway is colored green and Holland is orange, maybe because of good Prince William of Orange. I meant to ask Father but maybe it would be easier to ask Uncle Pieter.

Later Uncle Pieter knew why the soldiers were so thick on the Boompjes quay. He said it was because of the war fright.

Mother came in to kiss me good night and she said on Saturday if Father can get away we are going on a two-day holiday to Friesland to visit my Grandfather and Grandmother. Keetje promises to get well of her cold before Saturday. Grandfather and Grandmother are named Huyn and they have a fine house with a red-tiled roof which is very old. Many years ago the storks used to build nests in the large chimneys of their house but not now. There are not many storks any more and I don't know why. I saw some once in Delfshaven where the English Pilgrims stayed before they went to America. This was many years ago.

Uncle Pieter came over to smoke cigars and drink coffee with us after dinner but in the middle of everything my father had to run over to see a lapdog that was sick over at Mevrouw Klaes. Uncle Pieter was not as happy as usual. He talked about the war and made us turn on the radio to hear the news report even though Mother said she was sick of hearing about the awful state of the world. The radio said one thing that surprised everyone. All soldiers had to come back to the army at once, all their vacations were canceled. The poor soldiers. The announcer said not to be alarmed because this was only done to show our country's preparedness. There was going to be little railroad travel for anyone but soldiers from now on he said. I wonder if that means we shall have to drive our car to Friesland. Father does not like to drive.

It is very warm tonight and the rain goes on. I am writing this propped up in bed and I can hear Mother and Uncle Pieter talking downstairs. They are playing cards. I just heard several airplanes go over. They fly over all the time to Waalhaven airport which is not more than a few miles away. I have never been in an airplane in the air but I have sat in them when they were not flying. Keetje hasn't though. Mother and Father flew to England once two years ago. I used to be afraid one of the planes might fall on our house but I am no longer afraid. Our house has fifteen rooms and I have a room of my own. It is the largest house in the neighborhood except for the Baron's and Mevrouw Klaes. We have many blue tiles on the walls with pictures painted on them from olden times. Keetje waters the flowers in the window-boxes.

I have saved ten guilders toward my new bicycle. I get two guilders a week now for keeping the outside of the house clean though I do not have to scrub the steps or footwalk. This is Grietje's, the cook's, work. I want to buy an English bike and some day I want a Harley motor-bike like Jan Klaes has. He is seventeen and smokes as many cigars every day as my Father.

It is now nine o'clock and I am sleepy. Good night diary.

TODAY Keetje's cold is better but she did not go to school. I went as usual and Mijnheer van Speyck gave me a composition to do— *150 words* on the life of Erasmus by *Friday*. Now I wish I had done what Jan said and gone to the Hooger Burger School and not to the gymnasium. I would not have to study Latin. Next year I'll have Greek! Mijnheer van Speyck said I should go down and look at the statue of Erasmus if I needed to. I didn't go down because I have seen the statue many times on the way to the railroad station. M.v.R. was at school again today. She is the prettiest girl in school but not the brightest. I don't know whether she likes me or not. Her father is not a veterinary surgeon but just a plain surgeon for people.

Not much has happened today worth mentioning. Father came home early. He was cross because Mother was not back from the hospital. Mother is the head of the children's division of the hospital. Father scolded her and said he couldn't understand why she worked so hard and got herself all tired out when she didn't have to work at all. Mother said they needed her. Sometimes Father is very cross and then the whole house is cross and frightened. But when he is happy we are all very happy. Uncle Pieter did not come over at all today. I oiled and rubbed my fishing gear because the canal at Grandfather Huyn's is fine for fishing. I wish we could take M.v.R. with us. Maybe Keetje will ask her for me.

THIS has been a good day. I passed my examinations on Monday and Mijnheer van Speyck did not call on me to recite all day. He looks very unhappy about something. He has three sons in the army and one is a *grenadier en jagers* and helps guard the Queen at The Hague. Once he came to the school in uniform but Keetje said he was not as grand as her soldier. Uncle Pieter came today and talked a great deal. He says we are going to get into the war in spite of everything and that a government official at his hotel said the Germans had moved many troops from Bremen and Duesseldorf to our frontier. Father said *Dat is gek* [crazy] and Mother said please stop talking about the war. Uncle Pieter says no one worries and that's the trouble. Look what happened to Denmark and Norway and all the others he says. Father said you worry too much, you don't have enough to keep your mind occupied. Uncle Pieter doesn't work much, that's why. He has a gay life and lives at a big hotel in the center of Rotterdam. His son is in Java in the tobacco business and Uncle Pieter says he smokes so much just to help out his son's business, but Father says why do you smoke American cigars then? Uncle Pieter says because he likes American cigars.

I haven't written my life of Erasmus yet but I must do it soon. We had smoked herring for dinner and apricot tarts too, both things I like. I weighed myself today and have gained two pounds. My jacket is getting tight and short in the sleeves. Maybe I'll be tall yet. Uncle Pieter says it doesn't matter how tall you grow so long as there's something besides hair under your cap. Uncle Pieter is bald and short. Mother said he bought some false hair once but could never keep it on straight. Father has plenty of hair and so has Mother. All of us have except poor Uncle Pieter. My old bicycle had a flat tire today. I had to walk home because my patching kit was home. I'll be glad when I get my new one. M.v.R. has a new one. She can ride very fast for a girl. I saw her race a canal boat today and beat it easily. She was laughing with the policeman who stands by the white canal gates near our school.

Uncle Pieter has been reading from the printed card about how to prepare for war. The card is called WAT TE DOEN [what to do]. All evening he has been asking Mother and Father if they know what the card says to do. He gave the card to me and I am writing things down in my diary. There are many things to do and Mother has done some of them. She has taken everything out of the attic. The card says attics and top floors should be emptied so that they won't catch fire easily if war comes. Father says it is probably all foolish. The card says everyone should buy fire extinguishers and throw away all things like petrol the minute war comes. Bathtubs and water buckets should be kept full, it says. Every house should have sand buckets and spades with long handles. We have both but

we don't have a stirrup pump for pumping
water. We have first-aid kits though. The
WAT TE DOEN says many other things. It says
to stay away from windows if an air raid
comes. Disconnect the gas. Stay off streets. Be
orderly. Cover windows with heavy black
paper and use blue lamp bulbs inside. There
are many things to do like that and the paper
is signed by the burgemeester. Uncle Pieter
says he hasn't met anybody yet who knows
what the instructions say all the way through.

Uncle Pieter hardly talks about anything
but the war. He says the trouble is there aren't
enough air raid shelters. This he says is what
we get by living in a country half below sea
level. Not one person in a dozen can afford to
build a cellar and keep it pumped out and
water proof. There are not many cellars. We
have a small one and the Baron has a big one.
There are air raid shelters on the sand dunes
I know that and some above the ground made
out of cement. These are very funny looking.
They are shaped like half an eggshell. Uncle
Pieter says they are no protection and where

in hell will people go if war really comes. Uncle Pieter swears a lot. Mother says I must go to bed. I hope I don't have nightmares again about airplanes. They go over our house all night now, back and forth and back and forth.

SOMETHING terrible happened last night. War began!!! Uncle Pieter was *right*. The city has been *bombed* all day. Am writing this in the Baron's air-raid shelter. There are not many air-raid shelters here but the Baron and Father and Mevrouw Klaes had this one built for us and all our neighbors said it was a waste of money. This has been a terrible day and everything is upset and people are very sad and excited. This is what happened. Before daylight I woke up and for several minutes did not know what had happened. I could hear explosions and people were shouting under our windows. Mother came running in in her nightie and dressing gown and told me to get my coat on and come quickly. On the way downstairs she told me there was bombing going on but no one knew yet what it meant but she supposed it was war all right. The noise seemed very near. Father had Keetje in his arms and we hurried across the street to the Baron's and went down into his air-raid shelter. Betje and Brenda and Grietje, Mother said, were already gone to the Baron's. Father pointed toward the city and Mother nodded. There were great flames shooting up into the sky and beams of light from the searchlights and the sirens were going very loud. They are on the tops of buildings and have things on them to make them very loud. We could see bullets going up from our guns. The Baron's air-raid shelter was full of people, all our neighbors and some people I didn't know. They were all talking loudly and no one was dressed, just coats over their nightclothes. Keetje began to cry and Father whispered something to her and kissed her and she stopped. Finally she went to sleep in his arms. We waited about two hours. At first most people thought the noise was only practice. All the time people kept running outside and coming back with news. It was war all right and the radio was giving the alarm and calling all the time for all men in the reserves to report for duty at the nearest place. The radio said this over and over. It was very exciting. The bombing kept on all the time, boom—boom—boom, and everyone said they were falling on Waalhaven, the air-port, which is only about five miles away. The Baron went upstairs and began telephoning. The voices on the radio sounded strange and terribly excited. Father put Keetje into Mother's arms and went away. A few minutes later he came back dressed and carrying a gas mask and a knapsack. He kissed Mother and Keetje and me very hard and then hurried out. He shouted back something about taking care of his animals and Mother nodded and told him to be careful, *please*.

After the radio called for the men they all left the shelter and there was no one but the old men and the women and children. At six-thirty the radio said the bombing was over. We all went outside and were glad to get out. I wasn't tired or sleepy now but I wanted to see what was going on. Everything was just the same outside. The sun was beginning to come up and we could see it was going to be a fine day. We went home and Grietje made us some hot porridge and some hot milk and cheese. We ate very little. Mother did not eat at all. She was busy telephoning the hospital and other people. When she came into the dining-room she looked sad. Are the Germans coming I asked. Yes, but don't worry, we'll stop them Mother said. I have just talked to Uncle Pieter and he is all right she said but now I must go to the hospital. I want you to get dressed and go with Keetje and Brenda and Betje to the Baron's. Be sure you mind and stay in the shelter when the Baron asks you to. Keetje asked if we were to go to school and Mother said no, not today. She promised to come home as soon as she could. Betje and Brenda and Grietje all began to talk after Mother left and Betje telephoned her family and they were all right too except her brothers had gone away to fight. I went outside as soon as I was dressed. There was much smoke in the air and it made me feel sick for a minute. Brenda and Betje

27

took me over to the Baron's and Grietje came
a little later.

We did not go into the air-shelter at once.
There was too much to do. All along the street
people were running in and out of their
houses. Everyone was doing something. People
were digging long trenches away from their
cellars and some were shoveling dirt and sand
into big bags and throwing them up against
their houses. I asked Brenda what this was for
and she said it was to protect the houses from
bombs she guessed. I told her someone had better do that to our house and she said all right
come on and help. We left Keetje at the
Baron's and went back and got shovels. Brenda
and Betje and Grietje all worked with me to
dig a trench from our cellar to the garden so
that if a bomb hit our house we could get out
of the cellar if we were there and couldn't get
to the Baron's. We worked very hard for an
hour and didn't get much done because people
kept coming by and shouting things and a policeman came by with a paper for Father, but
Brenda said Father was gone. Many soldiers

came by. Then someone said the Queen was on the radio and we all stopped to listen. The Queen did not speak very long. I and my government will do our duty she said and she asked everyone not to get excited because of the Germans. She told the people that the Germans were wrong in coming into a peaceful country and that they would be driven out with God's help. We all felt better after hearing the Queen but the old men shook their heads. Pastor Opzoomer said we should go to the church and pray and that the bells in the Catholic Church were already ringing.

Just then Mijnheer van Helst ran in and said the Heinkels were coming again and it was true. The sirens started up and a little while later the bombs began to fall. We all stayed in the Baron's cellar. Ths noise was worse than it was before and nearer. I held Keetje's hand and she squeezed mine tight until it hurt. Once the cellar seemed to rock back and forth and the Baron said that was close. The people tried to talk but mostly they just waited. The bombing lasted an hour but it seemed longer.

One small child vomited. When the sirens gave the all-clear signal we came outside and looked around. We knew what the signals meant because we have had practice drills many times. A little way away there was a big wreck where a bomb had torn down the house of a man named Schaepman. I wanted to run over to the house and so did Brenda and Betje but we didn't go very near because the policemen came on bicycles and put up ropes. Then the firemen came, for the house was burning slowly. Someone said that Mijnheer Schaepman had been killed and his daughter hurt. The ambulance had come and taken them away. There were bricks and boards thrown all over the street. Some of the house was still standing and we could see a table with dishes on it and pictures hanging sideways on the walls. Poor people.

Some of the people at the Baron's began to start for home but the Baron said they had better wait. The radio began again and everyone waited to hear reports. The reports were very, very sad. Almost all the country had been bombed. The Hague, Amsterdam at the large Schiphol airport, Sliedrecht, Haarlem, Maastricht, Arnhem, Hook of Holland, Delft —just about everywhere. The Germans had bombed Belgium and Luxembourg too. I wondered about Father and Mother and if they were all right. The Germans had crossed the Maas River in the Southeast. It was terrible. The announcer then told about the Germans coming in parachutes and for citizens to be on the lookout and to arm themselves. Pastor Opzoomer came in again and said come out and look. We went out and he pointed to the sky away toward Waalhaven airport. It was filled with white specks floating down. Parachutists he said. People began to get more excited and some of the women began to cry. Many people said we should pack up and flee into the country but Pastor Opzoomer said no.

But some people went away. The streets were filled with bicycles and cars stood in front of the houses as far as I could see and women and children were running in and out putting things into the cars. Brenda and Betje watched them and talked together excitedly. Mevrouw van der Heide should be here Brenda said. She was talking about Mother. I wished Mother would come too. Keetje stamped her foot and said the Germans were awful people to make all this noise and to kill people. They were naughty she said. Mevrouw van Helst hugged her and said never mind, never mind, Keetje. It won't last.

About 10 o'clock Mother called up from the hospital and the Baron called me to the telephone. Mother wanted to know if we were all right and I asked her if she was all right. She said yes but that she wouldn't be home for a while as they were taking the sick children out of the hospital and away to the country away from the bombing. She said she would be home when she could and that Uncle Pieter was coming out to our house if he could get there. There were no more bombings by lunch time but over Waalhaven we could still see the parachutists coming down and we counted 21 bombers and 17 more planes go over on their way to the airport. They were flying high and we could not tell if they were our planes or German ones. We could hear guns booming in the distance and the sound of smaller guns across the north side of the River Maas.

We live on the south side of Rotterdam where the airport factories, wharves, and ships are. I wanted to get on my bicycle and go over to Rotterdam to see what had happened but of course Brenda wouldn't let me. Brenda won't ever let me do anything. We all stayed by the radio which was going all the time giving instructions and reports. News came that Waalhaven airport was in the hands of the Germans and then a few minutes later we heard this wasn't true. Parachutists were supposed to be dropping down in Sliedrecht and Delft. Delft is only 12½ miles from the capital. Pretty soon Haarlem, Geldermalsen and several other cities were talking about their bombing and parachutists. Military patrols, policemen, and citizens were warned that the parachutists might come down anywhere and to guard all roads and bridges and to shoot them. The Germans in parachutes wore Dutch

33

uniforms and other things the radio said. South Holland reported that some had come down in the black robes and flat hats of Dutch priests. This news made Pastor Opzoomer shake with anger until his face was redder than ever. Everyone began to get more and more angry as the radio talked on about fires and bombings and all the terrible things the Germans were doing. Fifteen hundred people had been killed in Rotterdam since 3 A.M. the radio said. The bombing we thought had lasted hours had lasted 27 minutes.

Even Brenda became angry and she shook her fist at the sky several times when planes went over. The radio said several German soldiers and parachutists were lying dead in de Boompjes street under the elm trees. Thought of my teacher and the life of Erasmus which I was supposed to turn in today. I wrote it last night and now I might just as well not have. Teacher is young and will be fighting but perhaps not very long and he never forgets anything.

Had hardly any lunch. The Baron's cook

who is very fat brought in some coffee and cakes and the older people had brandy but no one seemed hungry. Keetje ate quite well. She has always liked cakes. All afternoon we waited around not doing much but listening to the grown-ups talk and listening to the radio. People are all very kind to each other and friendly, even the ones who don't speak to each other usually. By five o'clock half of the fifty people at the Baron's house had gone home or run away in their cars to the country or somewhere. Anyway they were not around.

We got up a game with several other children playing soldiers and bombers. We took turns jumping off the high back steps holding umbrellas and pretending we were parachutists but we had to quit this because the grown-ups said it made them nervous. Just as it was getting dark the bombing started again. Mother came home on a bicycle which was not hers. She had taken the car in the morning but she said the roads were being barricaded and it was quicker to come by bicycle. We asked her many questions but she didn't talk much. She looked tired and white faced when she came into the air-shelter. The Baron and neighbors have brought in many cots and mattresses and a small electric stove on which coffee urns stand. It is damp and uncomfortable in the small shelter with so many people. It was all right this morning but it is not pleasant as time goes by. There are four old sick people near the stove but I don't know any of them though one is Mevrouw Klaes' mother I believe. The old sick people keep their eyes closed most of the time. Once in a while someone speaks to them and pulls the blankets up when they slip down. They are very silent and tired and dead looking.

Later

The air raid that came this time lasted 30 minutes. It was no better than the others but no worse. The Baron brought down a victrola and turned it on full blast to try to shut out the noise outside. Some of the music was German music, Mother said. How could it be from the same race who were attacking us she asked. The radio was off during the raid but it started up soon afterwards. The Premier of Holland, Dirk Jan de Geer, spoke and said for us to be confident because the Allies would help us and that hundreds of troops had been landed at Hoogezwaluwe, the big bridge which is between north and south Holland. When he finished, the radio said the landing field at Schiphol airdrome had been destroyed. Everyone was sad about this for it is our largest field. Had supper at the Baron's and settled down for the evening. All the lights have gone out upstairs and we are burning candles and lanterns down in the air-shelter.

Mother called the hospital after the last raid and Uncle Pieter but Uncle Pieter's hotel didn't answer. It is very hard to get anyone on the telephone. Everyone is calling everyone else after the raids are over to see if they are safe. The telephones are off during the raids. I hope Uncle Pieter is safe and Father too. Mother thinks Father has gone east to Maastricht and that's where the fighting is thickest the radio says though the bombing is bad everywhere.

Uncle Pieter came in after supper looking very sad. A big part of Coolsingle Street is gone he said. He came out on his bicycle and was stopped many times and made to show who he is. People who cannot prove who they are are being arrested. Uncle Pieter says the city of Rotterdam is damaged a great deal and that one German plane was shot down and landed in the streets. Many people have been killed and there is much sadness and many fires. Some people are frightened and some are very angry. Uncle Pieter says he saw para-chute troops coming down by the hundreds and that the Germans are landing troops all the time at Waalhaven airport, just going back and forth like the trolley cars. The Baron said it sounded impossible and many other men argued with Uncle Pieter and he said he knew, he had seen it, hadn't he.

Old Mijnheer van Helst said I thought we were prepared. Where's our army? Where are our aviators and things? How about our dikes,

trenches, pill-boxes, mined bridges and canals?
He was very angry. Uncle Pieter said they
were just where they were but no good against
the Germans. He said there was fighting in the
streets in Rotterdam and that Germans were
there barricaded in houses. It is terrible, terrible beyond belief, Uncle Pieter said. Mother
gave him a glass of gin and he drank it very
quickly and began to smoke his cigar. We all
sat around all evening talking about the war
and going outside and looking up at the smoke
in the sky over Rotterdam.

The sound of ambulances goes on all the
time but no more have come down our street
yet. The Baron says we three all have to stay in
the shelter tonight but many people want to
go home. Keetje looked tired and sleepy a little
while ago and Mother put her in a cot. There
is no bathroom, only two large basins in a
little room off the shelter. There are not
enough gas masks to go around and the grown-
ups have given theirs to the children. The
Baron has brought some coal in from a neigh-
bor's house—the kind made out of cocoanut

shells I think. This everyone is putting in wet bags, which is what the what to do instructions say. The wet bags are held up to the nose and this takes away gas they say. I don't know how. Our gas masks do not fit us very well and everyone hopes the Germans won't drop gas bombs. Not many people have bought gas masks yet. I put mine on and went to the mirror. I looked very funny in it and not at all like myself. Everything got very quiet after dark till nine o'clock. Keetje was asleep at last. Then the sirens sounded again and a new raid began. Several people went outside to watch it. Maybe they were not as frightened now. I went outside but was made to go back. I saw a little. The sky was streaked with lights from the searchlights looking for the Germans. We could hear the anti-aircraft fire and see red tracer bullets. The noise was worse than fireworks or thunder and went on all the time. It made my head ache and it made me a little sick to my stomach again. I wasn't frightened, but I felt a way I can't describe. Maybe I was frightened. The raid only lasted a few minutes this time. One bomb came down very near us and people all hurried back into the shelter. We heard the glass falling upstairs. Keetje sat up in her bed during the raid. She was neither all awake nor asleep but she was tired and her hair was stringy and her face pale and she wanted the noise stopped.

Finally it did stop, the sirens again saying come out. The Baron heard his cows mooing and his horses nickering in the stables. He took my hand and we walked down to the stone barn. We did not carry a lantern because the radio had been very strict in telling people to keep lights out after dark. The Baron called the horses by name and some of the cows. He told me the cows were so frightened by the bombing they could hardly be milked and that they had not given as much milk as usual at supper. They are good milk cows too according to Father who doctors them. Two of the horses were loose in their stalls. Their eyes looked frightened and wild when the Baron struck a match, and they kept on whinnying softly. They sounded like

Keetje crying in her sleep. There are some pets, dogs and cats, in the air-shelter, and they are very upset when the bombing goes on. Mevrouw Klaes' Pekinese was the only dog whose hair didn't stand up. Dop's dog kept howling and walking back and forth all during the raid. He snapped at Dop when Dop tried to comfort him and Dop was very surprised and said he had never done anything like that before.

I am getting very sleepy but I hate to go to bed and miss anything. Mother says I must lie down now. People are still talking. The radio is not going any more tonight because it might direct the Germans. There goes an ambulance siren again. Uncle Pieter says the English and French will have to help us because we can't have another day like this one. I hope we don't. Mother looks so tired and worried. She is probably thinking about Father but she hasn't said anything except that we must be brave and not show we are frightened because of the other people.

May 11, 1940

THIS was another bad day. The war didn't stop but got worse everywhere. Mother says the Germans have taken all of North Holland and she tried to telephone Grandfather and Grandmother Huyn but the telephone connections are gone now for good to that part of Friesland. Today was not like yesterday although the bombing and trouble are the same. It is now night and I am going to write what happened all day. We are in the air-shelter again. People are not talking as much as yesterday. Everyone is very tired from working. Yesterday no one knew what to do because the war had come so quickly but today we all worked, even the Baron and Uncle Pieter. The radio told citizens what to do to protect themselves. We have been piling sandbags around the houses and digging trenches away from cellars and laying in lots of food. Mother went to the bank this morning to get some money in case we had to leave but there was a long line and no one could take out more than two thousand guilders. There have been many air raids but we worked on outside during some of them. Soldiers are patrolling our little street, just going up and down which is patrolling. There are some soldiers on the housetops farther away. They are looking for parachutists and Dutch Nazis. A few people have tin or steel helmets like the soldiers but I wore a kettle over my head and so did many other people. We do this to keep from getting hit by shrapnel from the anti-aircraft guns and machine guns. People look very funny going around wearing kettles and pots over their heads and Keetje's keeps falling off all the time. The trolley cars have stopped running, to save electricity, the Baron says, and there is no drinking water in any of the houses in our section because the Germans blew up some of the water pipes yesterday. The telephone is not working either and all letters and telegrams have stopped coming. This is because of

the traitors and parachutists. The radio says
that no one is to go on the streets after 8:30
tonight unless he has the proper papers and
not to go anyway unless it's absolutely neces-
sary. There were seven air raid alarms between
9 this morning and supper. The radio says not
to depend on sirens for warning because some
of the traitors are giving false alarms. Uncle
Pieter is furious about this and says he will
shoot all traitors on sight and he has an army
pistol to do it with too. He carries it inside
his coat. There are not so many people here
tonight because some of them were called out
to fight fires and stand guard and help rescue
and dig for people in fallen buildings. I wish
I could do more.

This afternoon we saw our first parachutist.
We were pasting strips of paper across the
Baron's windows—the ones not broken—and
across the windows of our own house so they
won't break any more when the bombs come.
About half of them were broken in all the
houses around here yesterday. The parachutist
came down at three o'clock. About fifty came

down at once. This one was separated from the others. We saw the planes drop them but they seemed far away at first. Keetje was the first to see him because she was not doing much work. Mijnheer van Helst was near Keetje and when he saw the parachutist he called out to the women to go inside and then ran toward the man. The man came down behind the Baron's barn. We saw Mijnheer van Helst take out his pistol and aim and then he fired three times. He came back a moment later looking very sad and said the German was shot. The Baron and several others ran forward to see the German but Brenda kept me from going. Heintje Klaes went and came back and said the German was really dead and he was glad. Mijnheer van Helst didn't look glad and his hands were trembling. He is an old and very kind man and not used to shooting people the way regular soldiers do.

The parachutist, Heintje said, wore a one-piece green suit like coveralls and his uniform was like a pair of ski pants. He had a flying eagle on his helmet which was of metal. The

Baron brought back the helmet and he said someone could use this but no one wanted to put it on. Heintje got it later and is wearing it now. It is too big for him and he looks silly in it. Heintje is pretty silly looking anyway and his eyes stick out like tulip bulbs most of the time. Mijnvrouw Klaes went out to see the dead parachutist and came back very excited. She swore she knew him and that he was named Friedrich Buehler and had grown up in Holland after the other war. This caused a great deal of talk and excitement and Uncle Pieter said "the damned ungrateful swine. We took their war babies and fed them and this is what we get back." Some soldiers came and took the dead parachutist away.

Some more parachutists came down later in the afternoon. They landed nearer this time and right after they came down a squad of soldiers came running down our street toward the warehouses on the river. The Baron yelled at them but they did not stop. Later we heard firing and the warehouse was on fire. The soldiers came back and this time they stopped.

The Germans had come down and run into an old deserted building on the wharf. They had set up their machine guns and our soldiers had driven them out with hand grenades and set the building on fire. They also caught a man on top of a house they said who was signaling to the parachutists. The soldiers said the Germans were doing this all over Holland, coming down and taking over houses and shooting from them at citizens or whoever passed. The soldiers looked very tired. They only stopped for a minute and then went on. Mother has been gone all day and Betje and Grietje and Brenda have been busy storing all the pictures and nice things of our house in the cellar and burying some of the silver where the Germans cannot get it if they come.

The Germans have been bombing all day and I have seen several bombs drop out of the planes. They look small so far away and are only big when they explode I guess. Some of our planes always go up to fight them and they make small puffs of smoke in the air when they fire at each other, and the planes dive around

the sky at each other. None of the dive bombers have come very near but I have heard them
coming down across the river and the sound
is an awful roar. Some of the German planes
dropped pieces of paper today and Max Blok
brought one of the papers into our air-shelter. It said many things in Dutch and was
written by the Germans. It said the Germans
came as friends and they were sorry to be
doing what they were doing but they had to
protect us from the English and the French.
This made everyone laugh at first and made
them angry too. The paper also said that we
should stop fighting for it was foolish and
crazy for us to go on fighting when our country was almost completely beaten. Why did
we want to fight against our friends the Germans, the paper asked. Our friends the Germans, Mijnheer van Helst said, spitting. He
stuck the paper on the wall and ran his pencil
through it.

The radio came on before supper and said
that most of the west of Holland from the
Zuider Zee down to the River Yssel and

through the peat bogs had been flooded but the Germans were using rubber boats and still coming. The second water-line had been broken through by the Germans but the Dutch forces were fighting bravely and would go on. Several big important bridges had been captured by parachutists before they could be blown up the radio said but Dutch soldiers will get them back. Many soldiers are being killed on both sides and there is much trouble from bombing in Amsterdam. The Bethlehem hospital in Amsterdam has been all torn up. I was born in this hospital but of course I do not remember that. Mother pointed it out to me one time when we were in Amsterdam visiting the museum. The things the radio said are not very good. The Germans seem to be about everywhere. They have taken Waalhaven airport now and Schiphol and several others and are bringing troops back and forth. One plane was shot down with a horse in it which the radio said the German commander had brought for his victory parade. Citizens are warned to stay off the streets but to report any signs of shooting from private homes as some bad Dutch Nazis are helping the Germans.

Later, the same day

The worst air-raid of all has just come. About half the houses on our street are gone. One bomb landed on the lawn by our air-shelter and one side of the shelter is caved in but the Baron and others are repairing it now. Mevrouw Hartog broke down and cried during the air-raid and got everyone very nervous when she yelled. I think she almost went crazy.

Heintje Klaes was killed! He went outside to see the light from the big flares and incendiary bombs and didn't come back. He slipped out. Heintje was not afraid of anything but the bombs got him. The whole house rocked when the bombs came close. We put our fingers in our ears but it didn't help much. The fire wagons are working outside now and half the people in the air-shelter including Uncle Pieter have gone out. I went out for a while and they were taking dead people out of the bombed houses. Uncle Pieter sent me back to stay with Keetje. There is a funny smell in the air like burnt meat and a funny yellow light all over the country from the incendiary bombs. Three men were killed trying to get a bomb away that hadn't gone off yet. One of the men was our postmaster and I loved him very much. He gave me my first bicycle ride. It is awful to watch the people standing by their bombed houses. They don't do much. They just walk around and look at them and look sad and tired. I guess there isn't anything else they can do, but it seems awful.

Our house wasn't hit but the street in front of it between our house and the Baron's is just a great big hole and all the cobblestones are thrown up on our lawn and the Baron's until it doesn't look as if there ever was a street there. Mother is going to be surprised when she sees it. The street was just made over last year and was very smooth and nice.

At the end of our street the water is coming

in where the canal locks were hit and I guess it will just keep running over the land until it is fixed. No one does anything about it because there are too many people to be helped and fires to fight. Twelve people on our street were killed and I knew every one of them but I knew Heintje best. Mevrouw Klaes has been crying ever since the bombing. Some people prayed all the time and some sang the national anthem and some just sat and stared. A woman who is very sick with a bad heart looked as if she might die. She was very pale when she came and still is. Jan Klaes is Mevrouw Klaes' other son and he is fighting somewhere like my father is. I said a prayer to myself for Father and I hope God heard it in spite of all the noise. I told Uncle Pieter I had prayed but he didn't say anything, just laid his hand on my shoulder. Uncle Pieter has gone off to the hospital to try to find Mother. It is getting late and he is worried I think. I know he will find her. Keetje has gone to sleep again but she talks in her sleep and wakes up all the time asking if the war is over and things like that.

53

Poor Keetje, she is so little and doesn't know what is happening. I think I do and it is worse than anything I ever heard about and worse than the worst fight in the cinema. The ambulances coming and going and so many dead people make it hard for me not to cry. I did cry some while the bombing was going on but so many other little children were that no one noticed me I think. I just got into bed with Keetje and hid my face. I was really frightened this time.

Later

Uncle Pieter came back. He didn't find Mother because she is dead. I can't believe it but Uncle Pieter wouldn't lie. We aren't going to tell Keetje yet. The ambulances are still screaming. I can't sleep or write any more now or anything.

I AM writing this in the morning as Keetje
and I wait for Uncle Pieter. He is taking us
to Dordrecht and then to Zeeland if we can
get there. I can't believe Mother is dead and
that we will never see her again. Mother was
killed when the Hospital was bombed. I cried
almost all night and I am ashamed of what I
did in front of everybody. I tried to run away
from Uncle Pieter after he told me about
Mother getting killed. I tried to get out in the
street to fight the Germans. I don't know what
all I did. I think I was crazy. I was all right
until the bombs started to fall around mid-
night and then I couldn't stand it. I know I
yelled and kicked and bit Uncle Pieter in the
hand but I don't know why. I think I was
crazy. I went to sleep later but I don't know
what time it was.

Today I am tired but everyone is so kind.

The Baron gave me two currant buns for breakfast, the last there were, I think, and some rusks and cocoa. I thought I wasn't hungry but I was. Keetje still doesn't know about Mother. She looks tired too and this morning she vomited again when there was hardly any bombing. That is why Uncle Pieter says we must go away, maybe to England if we can, or to America.

Uncle Pieter left very early and went across the river to try to get all the papers to get to England. I hope he is safe. It is hard to get across the river now and the soldiers are very strict.

There is an awful noise here this morning because Schnitzie, the Baron's cat, ran up the chimney last night during the terrible bombing and now he won't come down. He must be very frightened for he meouws very pitifully and he won't come down. The Baron has been trying to coax him by putting some fish on the end of a stick and running it up the chimney but Schnitzie is still up there and making crying noises.

The fires on the street are not all out yet. The air is still full of smoke and now the house is smoky inside. No one is talking very much today. Two of the old people died last night during the bombing. They were not hit by bombs. They just died. I heard the Baron say it's just as well. The Baron is sad today and his face, which is usually red and jolly, looks white and he has great dark circles under his eyes. The radio this morning says the Germans have come far into Holland and they are getting most of the bridges that aren't blown up. I don't know how Uncle Pieter expects us to get to Zeeland. No one understands why Holland is losing the war so easily. The first day people said we could hold out until the French and English would come. The Germans are using many new tricks, I think. A man came in this morning and said the Germans had taken one of our forts in the east by using a new kind of gas that makes the Dutch soldiers numb. Someone else said, Mijnheer van Helst, I think, that the Germans have a bomb so big that it tears up a whole city block at one time. He said the Germans have a fire thrower now that shoots out a long line of fire for a great distance. Almost everyone seems to think that the new kinds of guns and things the Germans have are the cause of all the trouble, but Uncle Pieter doesn't think so. He says they just have more of everything, that's all. Our defenses are fine he says except we didn't have enough anti-aircraft guns or planes. We are like every other country the Germans have beaten he says. We weren't expecting the war from the air or parachutists or tricks like that. Brenda has just come in with our traveling bags. We have to wait for Uncle Pieter. Brenda brought Dopfer, Keetje's big doll. Dopfer is very big and Keetje shouldn't try to take him but she wants to. She has been asking Brenda when Mother is coming, and is Mother going with us.

Later

We are in Dordrecht now and it is late in the afternoon. We had a terrible time getting here. We are waiting in a café with all our traveling bags. We may have to wait a long time. There are no rooms in the hotels here because so many people are in Dordrecht trying to get boats to Zeeland and other places. We wanted to go over the Moerdijk bridge by auto but the Germans have taken the bridge and we can't go that way. There is nothing to do but wait here. It has been a terrible day. We are lucky to be here I think. Dordrecht is only a few miles from our home. Usually it takes about a half hour on the big new double road. It took us six hours to get here today in Uncle Pieter's car. He has an American car, a Buick, and it cost about 8 thousand guilders. Uncle Pieter is quite gay and rich.

We left home at 10 o'clock this morning. I almost cried again and Keetje did cry because Mother didn't come to say good-by. She couldn't understand it. Many people kissed us and said good-by, some of them I hardly knew. The Baron gave me a handsome silver ring and I am wearing it now. Our house never looked prettier than when we drove away in spite of the smashed windows and other broken things and the big hole in the street. I hope we don't have to stay away long. Brenda kissed us many times. Betje went away yesterday to the South and Grietje too. They were going to walk all the way into the country to get away from the bombing because they do not have cars. We gave them our bicycles and they were glad to get them though of course our bicycles are too small for them. Grietje has lived with us ten years, almost all my life. I forgot to say that Schnitzie was still in the chimney when we left though he may be down by now. I hope so, for it was awful to hear him.

We had a hard time getting to Dordrecht. The road out of Rotterdam was full of people going South to get away from the bombing. The electric railways aren't running and there are many people walking and some had bicycles with pieces of baggage strapped on to them. There were many lorries full of things and soldiers on the road going both directions. Most of the soldiers were going toward Dordrecht to fight the Germans who were coming up that way. All the people looked very unhappy. There were many children. There were all kinds of people rich and poor, walking and riding. Some of them sat at the roadside and were taking off their shoes and rubbing their sore feet. Some of the children were being carried and some were being pushed along in baby carriages piled up with food and blankets and canvas bags and things like that.

Uncle Pieter worked his way through the crowd but he went slowly and carefully. He blew the horn a lot but no one paid much attention. Just outside Rotterdam we passed M.v.R.'s house. It had been hit by a bomb and was still smoking! I wonder where she is now. There were some black and white cows eating grass on the lawn. They must have broken through from the farmer's polder behind. It was a bright sunny day with just a few clouds. Every day since the war it has been sunny. It seems awful to have this all happen just when we were getting ready for a nice summer. The meadows were full of spring flowers of many kinds but in the middle of many meadows there were Dutch soldiers with machine guns and anti-aircraft guns. This is the time of year when the fishermen go into the North Sea to get herring but now they can't go. Many of the windmills are not going today because the mills are not running, since the men went to fight the Germans. The windmills by the polders were still running to keep the water out of the fields where the rye and buckwheat and barley grow. There were no bombings on the road but there was never a minute we didn't hear guns in the distance somewhere. Some of the farmers told us there was a bad bombing yesterday all along this same road. There were several big holes but not many. Many people asked us for a ride and Uncle Pieter took in four old people after he had refused some. He said he had to get us to Dordrecht, he couldn't take everybody though he wanted to.

About three o'clock some German planes came over. They were seaplanes going toward Dordrecht. They dropped no bombs but five of them dived down toward the road until we thought they were falling and then they shot at us with machine guns. We all got under the car and many people crawled in beside us. Other people threw themselves on the ground and dived into the roadside ditches for protection. The soldiers tried to shoot the pilots with their rifles. The planes kept going back and forth above us very low and loud and then suddenly they went away south. There was great confusion after they left. Several people were hit. One woman in front of us, a young woman, sat by the roadside holding her head and groaning. There was blood coming out of her head and a hole in the side. It made me sick. About fifty people were wounded and many were killed. Uncle Pieter helped the wounded all he could and then we hurried away. All the way down the road we saw wounded people and people just lying still in the road.

Once Uncle Pieter had to get out and move three bodies to the side to get by. It was awful. Many children were crying. People were trying to be brave and pretend nothing had happened but they were all very sad and angry. The Germans are cowards to shoot people who have no guns. When they drop bombs they don't know where they go but they just came down on the road and shot at us today. I hope those Germans in those planes fall out of the sky and never get home and are killed. There are no towns along the Dordrecht-Rotterdam highway for the poor wounded people to get to. Nothing more happened until we got near Dordrecht and then we heard firing again. We were stopped and had our papers looked at and told not to go into the city but to go around it as there was fighting in the center of the city because of the Dordrecht bridges and the parachutists who were there.

We left the main road and just as we turned off Uncle Pieter saw two small children sitting by the side of the road. They looked lost and unhappy and Uncle Pieter stopped. They wouldn't talk at first. Several other people in our car tried to make them talk. They just stood holding hands. They were a boy and a girl. The girl was the oldest. She was about as

tall as Keetje and with dimples like Keetje's.
The boy was much younger with yellow curls.
Uncle Pieter spoke very gently to them and
finally got them to talk after he gave them
some chocolate. They ate the chocolate
quickly. He asked where their parents were
and they said they didn't know, they thought
they were killed. Uncle Pieter asked them
where they were going and they didn't say
anything, just looked at him. When he asked
where they had spent the night they said they
didn't know and then said somewhere on the
road. They were very dirty and tired-looking.
Uncle Pieter sighed and shook his head and
said the car was full but we would have to
make it fuller. The two children didn't want
to go with us. In the car they held hands all
the time and looked straight ahead. All the
way to Dordrecht they didn't say a word. The
other people in the car spoke to them but the
children didn't answer. Uncle Pieter said they
were like two lost birds.

We had a hard time in Dordrecht. Uncle
Pieter got to the waterfront but then some of

our soldiers stopped him at the edge of town
and looked at his papers. They said he couldn't
drive the car in unless it was a government car.
All the people got out and thanked Uncle
Pieter. Uncle Pieter and Keetje and I and the
boy and girl went over to a little café. Uncle
Pieter started to walk in but the door was
locked. He pounded hard and shouted and
finally a man stuck his head out. I want to
leave these children with you, Uncle Pieter
said. Open up. A man let us in. He said he
kept the door locked because of the parachutists who might come down any time.
Uncle Pieter put some money in his hand and
said give these children something to eat and
don't let them out of your sight until I get
back. I'm going to find if there are any boats
for Vlissingen. Vlissingen is the place to get
boats for England. You won't find any, the
café-keeper said. Old Thys Voerman will find
me one, Uncle Pieter said. He'll *have* to.

Uncle Pieter was gone a long time and when
he came back he looked pleased and happy.
Late tonight we can get over to Vlissingen,

he said. The girl and boy we picked up on the road were still eating but Keetje and I had finished long ago. The children talked more after they finished eating. Uncle Pieter found out they were from right here in Dordrecht and their house had been bombed the night before. They had crawled out of the ruins and run away and stayed all night. They were so frightened that was why they didn't want to come back to Dordrecht. Uncle Pieter gave the café-keeper some money and told him to take care of the children until he found someone who knew them. The café-keeper said he would but he didn't want any money for doing a thing like that. Uncle Pieter shook hands with him and said he was a good man and God would bless him. The café-keeper asked how the war was in Rotterdam and shook his head when we told him. Many houses in Dordrecht were gone, he said, and many people killed. Dordrecht is a beautiful town and one of the oldest in Holland. Uncle Pieter and the café-keeper swore at the Germans.

All the time we talked we could hear guns

going in the distance. The café-keeper said the Germans had the Dordrecht bridges and Moerdijk and the Dutch were trying all day to get them back. We went up on the roof to watch, but we could not see much in the dark —just flashes of gunfire here and there. The café-keeper said some English troops had landed at Vlissingen, he thought, and more were coming, maybe we would win yet but we would have to get the bridge back over the Hollandsch Diep or Holland would be cut in two. The French were in Zeeland already, we were glad to hear.

At ten o'clock Uncle Pieter said it was time to go. He gave the car to the café-keeper and told him to guard it well for he didn't know how many days it would be until he got back.

We took our things out and walked up the street in the dark. Uncle Pieter stumbled many times. He does not see very well in the night-time because of the last war when he was gassed, I think. We were stopped twice by Dutch soldiers and had to show our papers. Uncle Pieter seemed to have the right papers, for we never had to wait long. The farther we went the more people we passed in the darkness. When we got to the place where the boat was there were hundreds of people trying to get on to the boat. After a long time Uncle Pieter found his friend and we got on a very small boat.

LATER. It took us many hours to get to Vlissingen. The boat sailed without lights. All the time I kept thinking of our friends at home and wondering if the bombs were falling. I thought about Mevrouw Klaes and the Baron and Brenda and of course about Father. I wondered about the animals and if the cat ever got out of the chimney. Poor thing. I almost wish we were back with them. It doesn't seem right that we should be so safe when they are still there where the bombs are. I told Uncle Pieter this and he said we were not safe yet. I found out later why. Dordrecht is on a big river or canal and when it ends and goes to the sea we had to pass the Moerdijk Bridge. The Germans were there and the canal is only 50 yards wide. I am glad I was asleep and did not know this until later.

Uncle Pieter says we are not running away,

we are just doing the sensible thing for Keetje's sake. He didn't say anything about me and I was glad because I had been trying all day to help and to prove I was not just a big baby the way I had been the night before when he told me about Mother. In Vlissingen nothing much happened all day except we waited for a boat and Uncle Pieter got places for us in spite of all the other refugees. We are going to England tomorrow night. We are going to sleep this afternoon because we didn't sleep much on the boat and haven't slept well since the war began which was only three days ago but seems longer. There are many soldiers in Vlissingen but no fighting and no Germans or parachutists yet.

UNCLE PIETER must have been very clever to get us on the boat with so many trying to get on. We have been on the boat an hour but it hasn't left yet. It is late at night. There are no lights on the outside of the boat but inside there is some light but the portholes are covered. The boat has started and I wish I could go out on deck. But this is not permitted.

Later

The boat slipped along in the darkness and we could hardly see a thing through the cabin windows. There is not a single light in Vlissingen because of the bombers. I wonder if the little boy and girl we left at the café in Dordrecht are all right now. I hope so. I feel very sorry for them. There are many people on the boat. No one talks, for it is against the rules.

There are no beds for us and we have to sit
up but Uncle Pieter has taken Keetje up in his
arms and she is asleep now.

Later

I've been asleep for several hours. I woke
up a little while ago. I had a terrible nightmare
about bombing and thought a bomber was
chasing me and Keetje around and around the
canals and we were on ice-skates and kept slip-
ping and falling and couldn't get away. The
nightmare was terrible. I was cold when I woke
up and Uncle Pieter wrapped his big coat
around me. We are sailing on.

Later

The boat has been tossing around a great
deal. I asked Uncle Pieter how long it will
take to get to England. He says a good while
because we have to go back and forth zigzag
to get through the mine fields in the water. I
am scared we might hit one and sink. I can't

swim very well and Keetje can't swim more than ten strokes without puffing. Uncle Pieter says not to think about it. I try not to but I keep thinking about it. I was very frightened when I heard a loud explosion ahead of us some time later. Our boat slowed down after that. I thought the bombers had come again but there was nothing in the sky. The boat's searchlights went on for a few seconds but I couldn't see what had happened. We found out a few minutes later. The boat ahead of us had struck a mine and been blown up. Our boat tried to pick up a few people from the water and did pick up some but not many. The Captain of the boat tried to find the others but he couldn't find many because he didn't want to have the lights on. I hate to think of all the people out there swimming in the cold sea while we are going on to England. I hope they don't all drown. This war is terrible. It kills just about everybody. I'm glad we're going to England where it will be quiet. I hope the Germans don't come there the way they did in Holland. I don't feel very well tonight. I have a bad headache and my stomach feels funny. Maybe I am going to be seasick but I think it's just from the bombing and everything. I forgot to say how nice Keetje was before we left Dordrecht. She gave her big doll, Dopfer, to the little girl. Keetje was nice to do this. She is often very selfish but she was good to do this. It seems funny to be out here on our way to England. I have always wanted to go to England but I never thought I would go so soon. I pray God will keep our Father safe. We could not bear to lose Father after what happened to Mother. Uncle Pieter is very good to take care of us while Father is away fighting the Germans. Today is Sunday. I just thought of it. At home we always go to church and take a walk or ride in the car on Sunday.

WE have been in England all morning. It was daylight almost when our boat got in. We landed at a place called Harwich. Everyone cheered and sang when we came into the harbor safely. We took the train to London, which took about three hours, and went to a place in the station where refugees have to go. There were many English people there to give us breakfast and to help us. They were all very cheerful and smiling.

Some of the refugees looked ill and very unhappy and lost. There were children there without any parents or relatives or friends. Some of the children were French and Belgian. There were several English doctors there and some of them spoke Dutch. They were helping to fix wounded people. Uncle Pieter has taken us to a hotel near the station. I am writing this in the hotel. Uncle Pieter says most

of the Dutch and Belgian and French refugees
are going to the country away from London
so that if the bombs come again they will be
safe. They will go to Ireland and Yorkshire
and the Isle of Man and places like that where
I have never been.

Uncle Pieter has gone away to send a cable
to Uncle Klaas in America and to see the
American Consul. Maybe we will go to America later, he says. If we do he is not going to
go with us. He is going back to Holland. I
suppose he has to get his car from the café-
keeper and to tell Father where we are. No one
can send a cable to Holland now. You can send
it but it doesn't do any good. It is fine to be
in this country where it is so quiet and peaceful the way home was.

Later

Uncle Pieter came in with an English newspaper. I can read some of it easily. A funny
thing happened. Queen Wilhelmina took a
boat from Zeeland yesterday too. It is all writ-

ten about in the English paper. The English King met her at Liverpool station and kissed her on both cheeks. Count Johan Paul van Limburg-Stirum, our minister to London, was there too. The Queen was probably very glad to see him but I didn't know she knew the English King well enough to let him kiss her on both cheeks. Crown Princess Juliana was there too, the paper says, and also Prince Bernhard and the Princess Beatrix who is two years old and Princess Irene who is just a baby.

There is a picture of them all in the paper and many soldiers standing around at attention. Some of them are Dutch soldiers. Princess Juliana is carrying Irene in her arms and Prince Bernhard and a nurse are carrying a box that the paper says is a gas-proof box for babies. It looks more like a puppy box than anything else. Little Beatrix must be in the box. Things must be very bad with our government if the Queen has come to England. Uncle Pieter says the Dutch government has moved from The Hague to London, the Cabinet and all. It must be hard to move the whole government. I imagine the Queen's boat was much larger than the one we came on. Yes, it was a battleship, the paper says. Keetje says she wishes we had come on the same boat with the Queen. So do I. Anyway we were in Zeeland at the same time.

Later

Uncle Pieter has just come back with terrible news. Holland has surrendered to the Germans. It is all in the newspapers. Uncle Pieter is almost crying. Ever since he came in he has been drinking and smoking and walking up and down. He says the fall of Holland threatens England and we must go to America if we can get a boat. Queen Wilhelmina, the paper says, is going to speak over the radio but we have no radio and cannot hear her. Uncle Pieter says maybe he won't be able to get back to Holland or find out any news of anything. I wonder where Father is. I hope he is all right and safe and can go back to doctoring his animals. I just asked Uncle

Pieter if we couldn't go back now that the war is over and he said never, never could we go back there while the Germans were there. He says it is worse than death for Hollanders to live as slaves. I hope the Germans don't make a slave out of Father. I don't think they could. Father gets very angry and he would not stand for it.

Keetje is feeling very tired and ill. Uncle Pieter is having some food sent up to her, some warm milk and toast and eggs. I am having roast beef and pudding here with Keetje and Uncle Pieter is going to eat later. We haven't seen much of London yet and we have to stay inside tomorrow and rest. This is a very large room with high ceilings. Keetje and I stay in here and Uncle Pieter stays beyond the double doors. We have a private bath and it is very nice and quiet. The windows are all covered with thick cloth because it is after dark and no light must be shown because of the Germans. Keetje says she hopes there won't be any noise tonight and that the Germans had better not come to London.

I wonder how the Baron and all our friends are. There was a dreadful bombing in Rotterdam today. The English newspaper says one-third of the city was destroyed. The post office and our biggest building, a place called the beehive. It was mostly in the business section and along the wharves. I hope the bombs didn't come to our street. The *Statendam,* a big boat, caught fire and the Holland-American buildings were hit, Uncle Pieter says. Rotterdam is beautiful and I don't see why the Germans should want to tear it down and hurt the people who have never hurt them. Mother would have hated to hear about this. She loved Rotterdam almost as much as her home in Friesland. She met Father the first time in Rotterdam before they were married. Uncle Pieter says I must turn off the light now. He is going downstairs to the bar to get some more gin. He likes Schiedam.

The Queen did not come over from Zeeland, Uncle Pieter says, but from Hook of Holland, so she was not near us after all!

WE have been in England many weeks. Now we are in Liverpool waiting for a boat to America. Uncle Pieter has heard from Uncle Klaas in America and he wants Keetje and me to come. Uncle Klaas had to cable the American Consul and his bankers in America had to do the same thing. Uncle Pieter had to get visas and things and all kinds of papers and pay a great deal of money, I think. A great fuss. We are having much fun in England but we miss Holland. Keetje was ill for a week in the hotel in London. A doctor came to see her and said she was nervous. He gave her some medicine. He was very kind. He wouldn't let Uncle Pieter pay him anything. He said it was his pleasure and his gift to gallant Holland. Uncle Pieter argued with him but the kind doctor said no. Uncle Pieter says the English are just that way and good enough people when you know them.

Dear Uncle Pieter. He is so sad about Holland and so good to us. We have done so many things. In London he took us everywhere. The policemen—*bobbies* they are called!—are very funny and big and polite. We asked them many questions on walks when we got lost. We used to take taxis everywhere but now we use the little trams. All over London there are many things for war. Sand-bags everywhere. They were banked around the British Museum the day we went. The Museum has big pillars outside and many heavy doors before you get inside. Uncle Pieter was surprised to see so many people inside reading while there is a war on. There are many trenches everywhere and sand-bags at St. Paul's, a big church. In the gardens at Kensington there were many flowers but trenches too.

There are big black and white posters everywhere with ARP printed on them. This means Air Raid Precautions. People all carry gas-masks and we have them now. They were fitted on us by a nice woman in London. The gas masks have long snouts and look as funny as the Dutch ones. They have straps to hold them on. We must never carry them by the straps because they stretch and might let the gas in. That's what the woman said who gave them to us. Uncle Pieter put his on yesterday for the first time and looked at himself. He said he looked no better at all with it than without it. I laughed and he laughed too. I was glad to see him laugh for he has been so sad since he found out that one-fourth of our army was killed. When he reads the newspapers about the war he gets sadder and sadder. We haven't heard from Father.

When Belgium fell Uncle Pieter was almost sick. I saw a funny dog today. It was an English sheep dog, Uncle Pieter said. Keetje thought it was a bear that had escaped from the zoo. Keetje asked if the animals had gas masks too and Uncle Pieter said no. It is a shame they don't have. We had tea at the zoo with bread and butter and strawberry jam. I tasted Keetje's milk and it was good but not so good as the milk from the Baron's cows.

There are no street lights in England after

dark. We are getting very tired of the dark but not as tired as we were. We have only been out once late at night. We were in a taxi with Uncle Pieter coming home from the Mickey Mouse cinema. There are no crossing lights except little shaded crosses no bigger than a button. It is very exciting going along in the dark. In the daylight we have gone into the country. The roads are all fixed to stop the Germans. There are many barricades and trenches and tank traps. We have seen many lorries in the streets filled with big searchlights and guns and soldiers.

My English is improving. I practice it on the chambermaid. So does Keetje. Keetje gets more practice than I do because everyone stops to talk with her. She is very cute-looking in the new sailor hat Uncle Pieter bought her. Uncle Pieter is trying to speak English with us too so that we can get used to it but he forgets half the time and talks Dutch. Liverpool is not so big as London. It has many boats, though, and we like to go down to the wharves because they remind us of dear Holland. We are staying at a big hotel named the Adelphi. Everything in it is big. The bathtub is almost big enough to swim in and Keetje tried it and took a few strokes. The dining-room is big too.

Uncle Pieter has just come in with news. He says I must stop writing now. He has just had news from the ticket office that we have a passage and will leave sometime soon. He says he cannot go to see us off as it is against the rules because of the war. The ticket man is sending someone for us. I asked him the name of the boat and he said he didn't know that either because the ticket office couldn't let any secrets out because of the Germans. I must stop and help Keetje and Uncle Pieter pack. I hate to leave England. I have had a good time here and I hope the Germans never do to England what they did to Holland. Good-by, England. We have to leave you just as we were beginning to love you. I suppose we will have to get used to having new homes since we can't go back to our own dear home in Holland.

July 3, 1940

WE are on the boat now. We sailed yesterday sometime after dark. We had to wait many hours on the dock with the ticket man who told us animal stories. It was hard to leave Uncle Pieter. He kissed us many times and hugged us hard. He is going to let us know about Father if he gets back to Holland. Uncle Klaas will meet us in New York. We are on a big boat and there are many other children going to America. There are so many people going away because of the war that some of them have to sleep in bunks in the smoking rooms and halls. Everything is very strict on this English boat. Before we sailed a sailor told us what we could do and what we couldn't. We are not allowed on deck after the trumpet sounds in the evening. All the portholes are fastened tight and can't be opened. They are covered with thick cloths to blot out the light.

The ship doesn't even have lights on it to see by at night because of the submarines. The English sailor said no one could smoke on deck at night. A lighted cigarette can be seen two miles at sea, he says. If anyone disobeys he will be severely punished and put in a room and locked up for the rest of the trip.

There are double doors at the dining salon and we go in on the side so the lights don't show. There are many ships sailing beside us. We counted twenty. Six carry passengers and the rest are going along to keep the submarines away. There are torpedo boats, warships, and one airplane carrier. They keep very near us all the time and we wave back and forth. The boats are all painted gray so they will be hard to see in the water. Everyone is afraid of the German submarines. The English Captain says for me not to worry because anyone who was born around as much water as we have in Holland just couldn't be drowned. He is a nice man and is always making jokes. There are two other Dutch children on the boat. They came from The Hague. Their father is working for the goverment. We speak Dutch together just to rest our tongues. We practice J's and th's on each other. Keetje has been seasick ever since we left but the Captain says she will be better when we get away from Ireland. He says he will be too because most of the submarines stay around here.

I have never been on such a big boat. I have been on many boats on canals but this one is like the Adelphi Hotel in Liverpool only it wobbles. A man was caught smoking a cigarette today and put into a room and locked up just as the sailor said he would be. Many boys in Holland smoke at my age but I do not. There goes the bell for dinner and I am very hungry, and Keetje is pulling at my sleeve. She feels like eating tonight.

I HAVE not written in my diary for so long.
Not since I got to America. Uncle Klaas and
Aunt Helen met us. Aunt Helen is an American with long red fingernails and a very pretty
face. Our boat came in to New York at night
on the tenth day after we left England. We
came slowly because our boat had to take a
longer way because of the war. We stayed all
night in the harbor. We thought New York
looked very exciting in the distance. There
were so many lights and they were all on. All
during the time we were in England there had
never been any lights at night in the streets.
It looked fine to see so many all going at once
with so many colors. Uncle Klaas took us off
the boat the next morning without waiting.
Some of the children who were ill had to be
taken off the boat somewhere else and some
had gone to a place called Ellis Island.

When we got through the customs we drove to Uncle Klaas's apartment on Morningside Heights. The streets were very exciting. I remember particularly when we crossed one and Uncle Klaas said this is Broadway. I came over here just to show you, he said. Aunt Helen said it is prettier at night. Uncle Klaas has a beautiful apartment that is very near the river. Maybe he took it because he is Dutch and always wants to be near some water.

We have been in America several weeks now. Keetje and I go to a private school. We like it very much although it was strange at first. There were many new words and studies, but not so many languages to learn as in Holland. I am learning to play football and other sports. Keetje likes the movies and the drugstore sodas best. Keetje seems very happy. Sometimes I think she has forgotten about Mother entirely. But I haven't. There is a girl in my class who reminds me of M.v.R. and who is even prettier. She has brown eyes and hair and is named Betty Anne. Everyone is very kind to us and I have been made a monitor at school. School hours are shorter in America. My English has improved and I have learned many new words that I never heard in England and some not in my dictionary.

Several letters have come from England from Uncle Pieter. He has not been able to get back to Holland. He is working for the English now and is a volunteer fire warden. Uncle Pieter says he misses us. He has had one letter from Father and we have had one. Father is safe and back in Rotterdam. The letter we got from him had a Swiss stamp. It must not have been seen by the Germans, Uncle Klaas says. Father tells about what Holland is like now. There is not much food and many things like coffee and cocoa cannot be bought. The Germans have done many things. They have changed the names of the Royal Museum and anything with the word royal in it to National. No taxis are running. None of the Dutch can listen on the radio to anything but Spanish, Italian and German programs without being fined 10,000 guilders and two years in prison. People have to stay home after

10 o'clock at night. The food is getting worse and worse. Father said not to worry, he would pull through. He wants to come to America. I wish he could and so does Keetje. We write to him often but we don't know whether he gets our letters. I will be so glad when the war is over.

Keetje and I are happy here and everything would be perfect if Father and Grandfather and Grandmother were here and of course Uncle Pieter. I haven't had very good marks at school. The doctor says I am nervous and can't concentrate very well yet because of the bombing but that I will be all right later. The American doctor was just like the English one Uncle Pieter had for Keetje. He wouldn't charge any money for taking care of me. He said, *this is on me,* which is slang but very kind. I think he is a good doctor for I know I *am* nervous sometimes.

Sometimes when airplanes go over I want to run and hide. One night when it was raining I woke up and heard the rain on the glass and was frightened. I thought I was back in

Holland and that what was striking the windows were pieces of bombs. That is why Uncle Klaas doesn't like it when people ask me about the war. When he saw the theme I was trying to write in English for my English class about the war in Holland he was angry. I heard him tell Aunt Helen that he thought it was dreadful and that he wanted Keetje and me to forget about the war. But I know I'll never forget about it anyway, or forget the Germans and how Mother died. I won't forget America either. It is a good country that has made us feel welcome. Keetje is looking over my shoulder as I write this and says why don't you say it's "swell," that's an American word.

I know one reason why I'll always love America. It's because of something that happened on the boat trip here. When we were one day away from New York all the battleships and boats that had brought us over so safely turned around and went back toward England. We were all alone and very frightened. I was frightened because I don't swim very well and Keetje can only do ten strokes

and they don't get her very far. When the
boats all turned back we could see how frightened everyone was. That's what made us
frightened. We weren't frightened before.
But then someone started yelling and pointing
at the sky. There was a big zeppelin over us.
It said United States Naval Patrol Number 14
in big letters. We all yelled and cheered. I
won't ever forget that number 14, and the
nice safe way it made us feel. The zeppelin
followed us and watched over us all the rest
of the way to America. And people have been
watching over us ever since and there haven't
been any bombings. Not one. And that is why
Keetje and I are happy now.